Nordic Walking

From Hiking to Fitness Trend

D0525122

Disclaimer

All possible care has been taken by the author in compiling the information contained in this book and by the publisher in checking its accuracy. Nonetheless, no liability can be assumed for possible errors contained in the book. Neither the author nor the publisher can be held responsible for the accuracy of the information in this book or for possible damages resulting from such information.

© Naumann & Göbel Verlagsgesellschaft mbH, a subsidiary of VEMAG Verlags- und Medien Aktiengesellschaft, Cologne

Author: Freya Norden
Translation from German to English: Jennifer Taylor-Gaida
Complete production: Naumann & Göbel Verlagsgesellschaft mbH, Cologne
Printed in China

Nordic Walking

From Hiking to Fitness Trend

CONTENTS

INTRODUCTION

An endurance sport takes Europe by storm: From "Ski Walking" to Nordic Walking

Walking with special poles in hand turns classic walking into an effective whole-body workout that is suitable for people of every age and level of fitness.

*H*ave you noticed yet? Increasing numbers of people of all ages in parks and forests are using walking sticks to get around – only these sticks look nothing like the compact wooden canes our grandfathers used to lean on. Nordic Walking is the name of this new fitness trend that's causing a sensation worldwide. Nordic Walking is not related to the sport of race walking that came into vogue a few years ago. Instead, the typical sequence of movements with its dynamic steps and energetic use of poles reveals that the roots of this new sport lie in cross-country skiing. In Finland, top athletes from cross-country and bi-athlon teams often kept fit during the summer by cross-country

walking using ski poles. With the development of easy-to-handle glass fibre/carbon poles in 1997, "Ski Walking" was ready to take its place as a year-round sport – one that was so uncomplicated that it proved irresistible. Three years later, Nordic Walking already topped jogging in popularity in Finland, and had spread to the neighbouring Scandinavian countries as well. In great strides, the new trend sport made its way through Central Europe, the United States and Japan.

And now Nordic Walkers are on the loose everywhere! Apart from jogging and walking, no other discipline has so captured the enthusiasm of a large and especially diverse group of people and been able to hold their interest for so long. Family doctors and health insurance providers are thrilled about the almost magical effect this popular new sport exercises on people, because "Nordic" walking is evidently capable of enticing previously sedentary people of all ages to regularly enjoy long exercise sessions. But not only beginners and those getting back into shape are choosing the new sport as their favourite – Nordic Walking also has plenty to offer serious athletes. Leaps and stretches of running, but also rapid walking in hilly or mountainous terrain, make training with poles attractive even for the most ambitious exercisers. The handy poles also support people with orthopaedic problems and help injured athletes get back into shape. Nordic Walking is therefore ideal after a period of rehabilitation as a lifetime leisure-time activity, and is also suitable as a gentle complement to competitive sports.

Nordic Walking has developed into a popular form of exercise, easy to start up and offering a wide range of positive physical benefits.

But enough speculating – it's time to try it out for yourself! If you have never tried walking with poles before, you should go easy the first time testing this unusual gait. After a Nordic Walking premiere, even well-trained athletes may experience sore muscles, proving how thoroughly all parts of the body are being exercised. See for yourself – get out there and have a go!

Simply relax:
Active breaks for strength
and energy

We get far too little exercise, and not just because of our overbooked lives and chronic lack of time due to stress on the job and at home. But there is always time to take a short break and get some exercise. Particularly in hectic times, it's important for us to retreat to "time oases" now and then. It's easier than you think: get moving and say goodbye to your old habits. Go without a third cup of coffee or a nap at your desk and escape your workplace for a while. Talk a walk through nature and breathe in deeply. Treat your body, spirit and soul to a few minutes of peace. Enjoy the movements of your legs, which lay still for so long under your desk. Move your arms in rhythm with your feet and

Make exercise a fixed part of your everyday routine, because an "alert" body also optimizes your performance at work.

step up your pace. Feel how good it is for you to get your circulation moving and the blood flowing through your body.

INTRODUCTION

Even if you only have ten minutes' time for a walk around your office building or a quick jaunt through a city park – allow yourself a short "rejuvenation break". Every step will pay off, and you will return to work wide awake and full of new energy. Exercise breaks are not lost time, because after you have "filled up" on oxygen, you will be able to work with greater concentration and efficiency. Breaks spent moving are often the secret behind power-packed creative talents and all those who seem able to work long days without tiring. You can rid yourself of pent-up

A step in the right direction: by taking part in regular endurance training, you build a strong foundation for health and well-being.

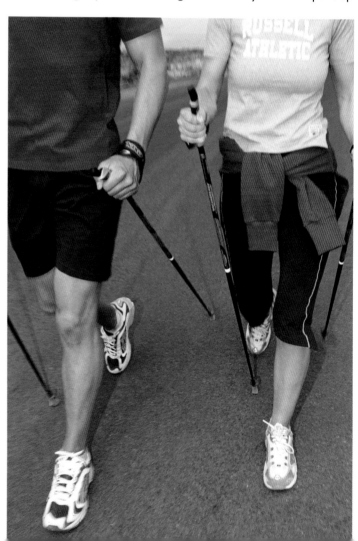

emotions and thoughts weighing heavily on your mind by taking a brisk stroll through natural surroundings, sometimes literally "walking your troubles away". Many things suddenly seem clearer once you gain a bit of time and distance and look at them again from a fresh perspective.

Mini-walks are wonderful small pick-me-ups during your busy workday. But these can't replace longer and more intensive exercise sessions. If you want to do something good for your health, to improve your fitness for your job and your family, or if you're dissatisfied with your weight, you should start a programme of regular exercise. In combination with a nutritious diet based on whole foods, endurance sport is your best choice. Steady endurance training has a particularly long-lasting effect on your body. Nordic Walking, walking, running, cycling or swimming strengthen and stabilise the cardiovascular system and help your body to work at top performance. With the right measure of endurance sport, your health is based on a sound foundation and you gain a feeling of well-being and joy simply to be alive.

Nordic Walking is especially fun in a group. Beginners in particular should walk at a pace at which they are still able to carry on a conversation.

"The Best Insurance is Endurance" was the motto of a campaign initiated in 1974 by the German Sports Federation and the German Track & Field Federation. In addition to numerous other efforts, the establishment of running clubs nationwide was designed to prevent the rise of diseases typical of modern civilisation, such as heart attacks and diabetes. Today, jogging groups meet in many cities, and they now offer many other endurance disciplines as well, such as walking and Nordic Walking. The participants know that exercising in a group is not only more fun, but also that time spent with like-minded sports enthusiasts flies by, while an impressive number of kilometres are racked up as well. As a solo (Nordic) Walker or lonesome runner, beginners in particular often encounter "start-up difficulties" and motivational problems. A running or walking group offers a feeling of security

and eases the first steps toward more active leisure-time choices. What's more, newcomers can learn a thing or two from the "old hands" and get plenty of valuable tips during shared walks. Find out about the running and walking clubs active in your city, or contact a sports association near you. There you can find out where and when endurance athletes meet in your vicinity.

Positive effects of endurance training

Endurance sports train general aerobic stamina and performance capability. The Greek word aerob means "with oxygen" and is used to describe metabolic processes that require oxygen to take place. Endurance athletes exercise for long periods in conditions of oxygen excess, thereby activating a large number of muscle groups. With regular endurance training, the heart learns to work more economically; the resting pulse sinks, which in turn eases the burden on the heart muscle. Medical studies have demonstrated that consistent endurance sport lowers blood pressure and significantly reduces the risk of heart attack.

Frequent and relatively long exercise sessions improve the performance of the lungs and enable deeper, more economical breathing. Musculature, organs and bones are supplied better with oxygen and nutrients, and metabolic by-products can be transported away more easily. The strengthened and optimally working immune system not only offers strong protection against infection, but is also better able to defend against tumours. And the best part is: as an endurance athlete, you can not only revel in a strong, well-proportioned body, but also enjoy a more even temper and a satisfying sense of well-being.

HEALTHY AND FIT WITH NORDIC WALKING

Swimming and cycling are wonderful and extremely effective endurance disciplines, but regular training is often made difficult by the need for prior organisation, or inclement weather. Are you looking for a sport you can do outdoors no matter what the weather, even in the colder part of the year? It should be simple and uncomplicated, something you can start up just by walking out the door? Then you should definitely try Nordic Walking! Passionate "pole walkers" appreciate this relaxing way to get fit from head to toe while enjoying the beauty of nature.

Nordic Walking poles are the perfect training partners and activate muscle groups that are often neglected. This kind of endurance training is also fun!

13

At a glance:
Why Nordic Walking is good for you

Break out of the vicious circle of laziness and bad habits! Nordic Walking makes it easy for you to start living a more mobile and healthy life. Your new sports equipment will motivate you to undertake regular walks through the countryside.

❑ Nordic Walking boosts your vitality: taking dynamic walks in the fresh air supplies your whole body with oxygen, while stimulating your heart and circulation.

❑ Regular training lowers your resting and working pulse rates and increases blood flow through the coronary arteries. Your heart can perform at a higher level. All of your organs – including the brain! – benefit from better circulation.

❑ Your body will start to form new capillaries, which optimises the supply of oxygen and nutrients to all parts of the body. The increased elasticity of the blood vessels lowers the risk of thrombosis and arteriosclerosis.

❑ The endurance sessions activate your metabolism; fat-burning enzymes multiply and help to sink blood lipids. Your basal metabolism rate rises, making it possible to reduce weight sensibly. Increased movement also promotes better digestion and prevents con-stipation.

❑ The immune system becomes stronger, and susceptibility to infections drops. You will suffer from fewer colds.

❑ Your stamina improves. Muscles, tendons and sinews are strengthened. Tense muscles relax. You will move more smoothly and gracefully and improve your co-ordination.

❑ Bone metabolism is boosted, making your bones sturdier. This also helps prevent osteoporosis. Cartilage around the joints thickens, and is able to withstand greater stresses.

❑ You feel younger longer – and look younger, too!

The renowned Cooper Institute in Dallas, Texas studied the effects of Nordic Walking in 2000 and compared its effectiveness with that of normal walking for fitness. The study showed that the test subjects who took up Nordic Walking burned up to 46 per cent more calories and took in a greater amount of oxygen than those who walked at the same speed. Fast-paced walking with poles is thus more effective and — if performed regularly — an effective weight loss method. The reasons are easy

Because it tangibly eases the burden placed on joints, Nordic Walking is especially suitable for people with orthopaedic problems.

to explain: through the use of the Nordic Walking poles, the muscles of the arms, back, chest and shoulders are activated in addition to the legs, and use up additional energy. Even after a training session has ended, fat metabolism continues at a high rate for some time.

With Nordic Walking, you can build attractive muscles in places that are not much affected by walking or jogging, even without weight training at a gym. Nordic Walking reactivates in particular the muscle groups in the chest, upper back and shoulder area, which are often neglected due to the one-sided movement and long periods of sitting that characterise everyday life for many of us. The movement sequence with the poles creates a natural and gentle alternation between tension

and loosening of the musculature, which is playfully strengthened almost without our noticing.

The musculoskeletal system also benefits from this gentle form of training: Nordic Walkers are in constant contact with the

Challenge your body and use muscle groups that you tend to disregard in everyday life.

ground, which is kinder to the musculoskeletal system than running, where the feet are repeatedly lifted off the ground and then brought down again, bearing three times the body's actual weight. Through the use of poles, Nordic Walkers distribute this weight more evenly between the arms and legs. This eases the burden on the musculoskeletal system by up to 30 per cent and makes the sport especially attractive for people who suffer from pain in the spine, knees or hips. Overweight people also profit from the extreme buffer function of the robust poles, which ensure that tendons and ligaments are subject to far less of a jarring impact.

The poles are most useful in uphill and downhill walking, for here they protect especially accident-prone zones such as the knees and back. Slightly hilly terrain is also particularly effective for strengthening the muscles. Cross-country walks offer the added benefit that they train the walkers' flexibility and coordination: since the dependable poles give people a feeling of greater security, they can tackle more difficult ground with greater élan. Movement is suddenly fun and not a chore anymore. As a newcomer among the "pole walkers", don't let yourself feel pressured to perform to certain standards or levels: Nordic Walking is an excellent way to increase your cardiovascular training step by step. Give yourself time to get to know the new sport, and enjoy the rhythmic, relaxing interplay of arms and legs, without overdoing it.

Your body has to adapt itself to increased exercise. Give it sufficient time to do so and pay attention to any "warning signals".

Don't try to jump in and take off at top speed right from the start! Especially if you have not exercised for a while, it is important to give yourself a chance to slowly get used to regular sport. Your cardiovascular and musculoskeletal systems will first have to adapt to the new challenges you are offering them. One of the best ways to get started is to participate in one of the many Nordic Walking courses on offer – just check with the sports stores, sports clubs or other organisations where you live. Besides, taking up a new exercise programme is twice the fun when you have company. Once you are adept at the movement sequence and your fitness level has improved thanks to regular training sessions, you can really take off!

WELL-OUTFITTED FOR NORDIC WALKING

Good shoes provide the highest level of comfort, supporting and guiding your foot optimally.

The Nordic Walker needs just three things for a good workout: a pair of good running or walking shoes, a pair of Nordic Walking poles and sports clothing appropriate for the respective weather. If you already have running or walking shoes, you can of course use these for your first few trial walks. But if you find you really enjoy the new sport and want to train more often, special walking shoes are highly recommended. Since the toes move upward more in walking than in running, the muscles of the shin are activated more thoroughly. A flatter sole in the heel area minimises the stress in this zone, protects the feet and gives you a more pleasant feeling while walking. Walking shoes also feature a sturdier outer material than running shoes and a sole construction that allows the foot to make a perfect rolling motion. Ask for advice in a reputable sport shoe store, or choose a high-quality running shoe that fits the special features of your own feet.

It is important to resist the temptation to try to save money

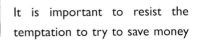

Don't compromise when it comes to buying shoes! Only the proper shoe can prevent injuries and make movement fun.

on shoes. Keep in mind that with each step you take, your feet bear from 1 to 1.5 times your body weight. After just a half hour of walking, your shoes have already been subjected to an overall load of 250 tons! These figures make it evident that care should be taken in choosing suitable "sports companions". A good shoe is robust, cushions impact and stabilises the foot's movement. An optimal fit will prevent uncomfortable rubbing and blisters, while a special last construction can correct common orthopaedic misalignments.

Your feet are unique

Every human moves differently and can be recognised by his or her own special, individual gait or walking style. Professionals distinguish between normal pronation, over-pronation and supination (under-pronation), and there are special running shoes available for each of these conditions. Normal pronates are actually in the minority; most people have some degree of biomechanical misalignment, such as flatfoot, splayfoot or high arches. A "normal" foot makes an ideal rolling movement from heel to toe and from outer to inner edge and usually requires only minimal support. Over-pronation is when the foot rolls inward too far after hitting the ground. In order to prevent the foot from rolling too far inward, shoes for over-pronates have extra support on the inner side of the heel. Shoes worn by over-pronates show stronger signs of wear on the inner side of the heel area than the outer side.

Looking for sturdy footwork:
What to look for when buying walking shoes

☐ *Gym shoes for ball sports or cross-training shoes are not suitable for runners, walkers or Nordic Walkers.*

☐ *Take your time when purchasing shoes and do your shopping in the afternoon. Your feet swell quite a bit during the day, so this will ensure that you don't choose a size that's too small. If you already own a pair of running shoes, you should bring these with you.*

☐ *Walk or run in the new shoes for a few metres, either in the shop or, even better, on the street to try them out.*

☐ *Double is better: buy two pairs of shoes from different manufacturers or in different models and wear them alternately. This ensures that joints, tendons and discs will not be subject to one-sided stresses, and it will give your musculoskeletal system the kind of variety that does it good, while minimising any orthopaedic risks.*

In people whose feet tend toward supination, the outer sole area in the fore and mid-foot zone is subject to the most stress. Arched feet or muscular weakness can be the causes of this more rarely seen misalignment. Supinates walk better in shoes with a stable heel cap and a reinforcement that reduces the stress on the foot's outer edge.

Feet deserve some special attention. After all, they carry an athlete reliably over every terrain, day after day, year after year. Walking barefoot on the beach is a treat for your feet.

WELL-OUTFITTED FOR NORDIC WALKING

And don't forget to take care of your feet after you return home from your Nordic Walking session! After all, their well-being is essential for your leisure-time enjoyment. Whenever possible, give your feet some fresh air and freedom of movement. Walk around outside barefoot in the summertime and enjoy the sensation of direct contact with a variety of different surfaces, such as grass or sand. This strengthens the foot's arch and other muscles. A foot-care cream is no luxury for an athlete, but rather an important way to prevent dry skin, pressure points and painful cracks that can completely ruin the fun of walking. Try to keep your toenails as short as possible in order to minimise friction. Special running socks are another worthwhile investment you may want to consider. They have no seams and are made with special soft toes and heels to afford optimal protection from irritation. What about a wellness day for your feet once in a while? Pamper your tried and true companions with a long massage and a relaxing footbath!

Don't neglect your most important walking accessories! Taking good care of your feet and toenails will save you from painful blisters and infections.

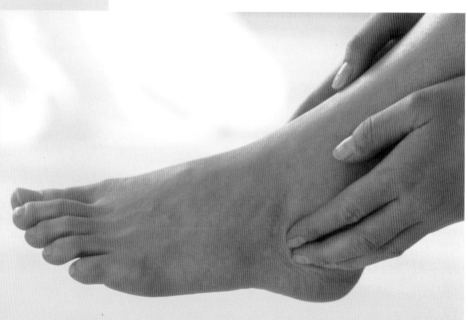

Sporty poles for maximum walking pleasure

You can buy Nordic Walking poles made of aluminium or a carbon/glass fibre mix in any well stocked sports store. They are longer than the ordinary walking stick, have hand-formed grips with straps to go around your wrists, and a metal point at the end. As a Nordic Walker you should accept no compromises: cross-country or ski poles and hiking sticks are not suitable for this sport. Often, telescoping poles are recommended for all-round cross-country use. But these will give walkers little pleasure because they are too heavy and transmit too many vibrations to the musculoskeletal system.

Special poles make it all possible: walk wherever the spirit takes you – uphill with perfect propulsion, downhill with gentle support.

Kick off your Nordic Walking premiere with equipment designed exclusively for this discipline. Carbon poles are light in weight, have a long useful life and are extremely robust. They are lighter than aluminium poles and do a better job buffering vibrations. Metal poles not only make an unpleasantly loud "clicking" on hard surfaces; they also put more stress on the joints of the wrists, elbows and shoulders and

are less stable than carbon poles. On the plus side, metal poles can be adjusted in length so that they may be used by people of varying heights. Aluminium poles with a cushioning system are now also available.

Functional hand straps enable you to maintain constant, loose contact between hand and pole.

In order for you to take off at a brisk pace, your hands need something they can grasp hold of. The specially designed strap system attached to the handles of Nordic Walking poles ensures the perfect positioning of your hands and guides your hands in the proper transfer of forces during the push off and stabbing phase with the poles. The strap should allow some room for movement and should not hinder the motion of your hands on the grip in any way. The best-designed handles have straps that are infinitely adjustable and have a hook and loop fastener for quick release.

Advanced Nordic Walkers tend to go for longer poles. This enables them to lengthen their stride and train more intensively.

Well thought-through from top to bottom, a good Nordic Walking pole also has a robust tip made of hard metal. This hardwearing material ensures secure footing on forest trails and fields, while also doing the job on gravel paths or stony stretches. For extremely dense ground surfaces and especially asphalt, rubber pads – which you can easily carry with you in your jacket or trouser pockets – can be attached to the poles' tips in no time. They give you firm footing and cushioning and, with their large-surface profile, also prevent slipping on a smooth surface.

For the best in walking, a pole that is just the right size for your height is essential. A clean and effective walking technique depends to a great extent on the right length of pole. Nordic Walking poles can be purchased in various lengths, from 100 to 140 cm. There are two ways to determine the right size:

❑ Stand the poles up vertically in front of you. If your upper arm is at a 90-degree angle to your lower arm, the poles are the right length.
❑ Multiply your height by 0.7. The result is the recommended pole length in centimetres.

If you want to be on the safe side, ask a professional for advice. Human arms and legs obviously don't come in standard lengths, and it might be that, despite calculating the pole length correctly, you still don't feel comfortable using your new equipment. A good feeling gives you security and is the only way to ensure lasting pleasure with Nordic Walking.

The right clothing for any weather

There is no such thing as bad weather, only bad clothing. With functional sport fabrics, endurance athletes can be active year-round.

With modern functional clothing, it is not difficult to always be dressed appropriately for walking in any weather. Breathable artificial fibres differ from cotton in their ability to transport moisture away from the body to the outside of the garment, rather than absorbing and holding moisture close to the body, as cotton does. Walkers can take advantage of the huge selection of functional running clothes available today, including under-

garments, t-shirts and turtlenecks, fleece jerseys and sports jackets. There are also exercise trousers in varying lengths and even special socks, caps and gloves for active outdoor sports.

The benefit of the new high-tech materials is in their method of action: when the body perspires during sports, the moisture is wicked outward, while air from the outside can penetrate the fibres to cool the body. This prevents athletes from becoming chilled due to evaporation of perspiration, as used to be the case. There's no longer any need for exercising outdoors to be associated with either freezing or sweating. Another plus is that modern sports clothing dries very quickly after washing, and is ready to be worn again in no time. This also qualifies it for sports activities extending over several days.

Don't cut corners when purchasing functional textiles: purchase several pieces at once, which you can wear with each other in various combinations, depending on the weather conditions. The individual garments can be layered on top of each other like the skins of an onion, guaranteeing wearing comfort as well as protection from the elements and well-being. This method only works, however, when it is not interspersed by garments that are not made of breathable materials. Finally, here's a tip from long experience: try not to dress too warmly when taking off on a Nordic Walking jaunt. After just a few minutes, you will have warmed up and will suffer if you have to carry around too much textile ballast.

With appropriate clothing, you can walk in any weather.

Please note: lightweight functional fleece jerseys obviously offer less protection from rain than a rain jacket. But make sure your jacket is also made of "breathable" microfibre. Rainwear labelled "waterproof" is unsuitable for use during exercise: as soon as you warm up and begin perspiring, you will feel as if you're trapped in a sweatbox.

MOVING NATURALLY WITH NORDIC WALKING

C urious? It's time to get moving: just slip on your shoes and choose an area that's not too heavily frequented for your first attempts at walking with poles.

How to walk correctly

Beginning is easy, because Nordic Walking promotes your natural stride through the use of poles.

The best choice of terrain to start off is a flat stretch that allows you to control the sequence of steps carefully. Don't worry too much or feel cramped – after all, you are perfectly able to walk! The simultaneous use of the poles will soon be second nature to you. Nordic Walking has plenty to offer, provided you carry out

the technique correctly. Your muscles will become stronger as a result of the powerful interplay of legs and arms. If your steps are brisk and you use your arms correctly to operate the poles, excess weight will soon start to come off. Furthermore, walking is much more fun with the right technique, and once you have a sound foundation, you can start to try out all of the exciting variants that Nordic Walking has to offer.

Precision pays off: the right technique ensures that your body derives optimal benefits.

Just like race walking, the basics of Nordic Walking are easy to learn. In comparison, however, the length of your stride will be longer when Nordic Walking, and your arms will move less. The natural, diagonal stride is supported by the poles, held close to your body, as in cross-country skiing. The left leg and right arm swing loosely forward. When the heel of the left foot strikes the ground, the pole movement of the right arm is triggered. The positions then switch, and the right heel strikes the ground simultaneously with the left pole.

Let's have a look at what the feet are doing: as in walking, the outer side of the heel makes contact with the ground first, and the foot then rolls over the entire length of the sole. This supporting phase ends with a powerful push-off that originates from the ball of the foot and the toes. This, together with energetic use of the poles, is the prerequisite for a long and dynamic gait. Your shoulders should remain relaxed and loose as the arms are moving, and bending the upper body forward slightly allows your musculature to work more effectively.

The interplay of arm and leg movements is key. Swinging your arms strongly makes your pace more dynamic.

Are you afraid of getting out of breath? Support your breath by deliberately breathing in deeply in rhythm with the pace of your steps. Pay attention to your breathing and find the breathing rhythm that is most comfortable for you – this will be your own natural breathing in keeping with your body's efforts. If you get out of breath, it's a sign that you're going too fast and are in danger of overstraining your muscles.

Step-by-Step

Take the first steps practicing the movement sequence without using your poles; just let them hang loosely from the straps for now. Your arms will automatically swing opposite to the movements of your legs when you walk. Swing your arms a little more deliberately, but easily, in the rhythm of your steps. You begin each step by setting down your heel. Now increase the amplitude of your arm swings.

The forward hand grasps the pole and pushes it into the ground, while the rear hand opens to enable that arm to stretch backward. The left pole is pushed off, the left arm stretched backward and the handle released.

Take a few moments to get a feeling for the coordination of your arms and legs. Now grasp the handles of your poles loosely and move your arms further forward, until they have reached the level of your chest. Push the pole far back on the backward movement. This will slowly increase the pressure on the straps. Now you can deliberately stick the tips of the poles into the ground and use the thrust you gain thereby to increase your

31

walking speed. You will find that you automatically lengthen your stride and hold onto the poles tighter. Tempo comes from a powerful push-off.

The pulling phase for the right arm and at the same time push-off by the left foot. The right leg and left arm swing forward.

Just as in cross-country skiing, you keep your arms with the poles close to your body. The tips of the poles always point diagonally backward at push-off, in order not to brake the forward motion. Your goal is to walk easily and yet dynamically. Once you've taken some time to get used to these basic techniques, try to open your hands after the backward push-off with the poles. This relaxes the muscles of the shoulders, arms and hands. The strap will prevent you from dropping the pole. When you have trained regularly for a time and your arm muscles have become accustomed to this form of movement, you will be able to use the poles with more and more skill, drawing your arms far back with relaxed, open hands. This not only makes you faster, but also strengthens your chest and arm muscles particular intensively.

The right arm is completely out-stretched, the pulling phase completed. The right leg moves forward, the right heel striking the ground, while the left arm brings the left pole into play.

Opening the right hand ends the use of the pole, and now it's time for the left arm to begin to push off.

How to ensure the right form

❑ Have you gotten out of step? Then pause for a moment and let the poles hang from their straps. Simply walk without them for a stretch and then take up the rhythm anew.

❑ Are you grasping the pole handle loosely? If you clench your pole tightly in your hand, your muscles can't relax. Undesirable consequences might be tension and overstrain in your lower arm or elbow area.

❑ Make sure you are moving your arms correctly. They should not be moving from the elbows only. The whole arm should swing forward from the shoulder down.

❑ Are you hardly moving forward, although you feel like you're working quite hard? While walking, push your foot deliberately into the ground all the way until your hip is as far back as possible, to get more forward thrust.

❑ Is your upper body completely perpendicular to the ground? Then the torso muscles can't be enlisted optimally in coordination with the arms. Lean forward slightly when walking for more power in your gait.

❑ Your pole tips should always point backward at a slant. This lets your arm muscles unfold their full power at the beginning of the pulling phase.

Nordic Walking across country

Are you now confident in your style with the poles? Then feel free to leave wide hiking trails behind you and take off across country! Cross-country walking wherever the spirit leads you is the greatest pleasure for Nordic Walkers. Walk uphill and downhill as you please, using the stocks to bravely master obstacles like streams and gullies.

Hilly or mountainous terrain is especially good for training strength and stamina. You have probably noticed on previous hiking trips that climbing really makes you feel your leg muscles at work. In Nordic Walking as well, inclines help to build muscle effectively. The thighs, calves and buttocks muscles stand to benefit the most from climbing. The upper body leans farther forward than on flat terrain, and the arms are used more intensively to support the legs' work. A powerful push-off with the ball of the foot gives you more "propulsion". With an increasing grade, your steps become shorter and the load on the leg muscles increases. Start out slowly and don't overdo it, especially if you haven't been walking for long. Before you undertake tours in mountainous regions, make sure you have built up a good endurance level and have the necessary technical skills at your disposal. A pulse monitor helps keep your speed in the optimal range and avoid overstrain.

With a bit of practise, your form will soon improve, and the poles will carry you safely over any terrain.

Rest your body weight on one or both of your poles and feel how the pressure on your legs and joints eases. Experiment "braking" with the poles.

What goes up must come down. As a Nordic Walker, your poles will do you a service here, because downhill walking actually taxes muscles and joints much more than climbing uphill. The poles not only help you gain secure footing, they also tangibly ease the burden on your knees. Always make sure to keep your centre of gravity as low as possible, and bend your knees slightly. This reduces your risk of falling. It is not possible to take large

steps when you are walking downhill. Always set the tips of your poles firmly into the ground behind your body and "brake" yourself by leaning back just slightly. During especially steep passages, you can stick the tips of the poles into the ground in front of your body to ease the burden on your legs.

TRAINING SENSIBLY

*N*ordic Walking certainly has very welcome effects on your body. But the health-promoting impact can only unfold to the fullest extent when you train regularly and for long enough stretches at a time. "Challenge yourself but don't overdo it" should be your motto. With just the right amount of effort, you can optimise your body's overall "operating system" and your fitness level.

A well thought-out training programme ensures that you build a solid foundation and make good progress.

You will really feel the difference when you decide to take up an endurance sport like Nordic Walking and get onto a regular training schedule. With every well-measured dose of movement, your body will change a bit more and adapt to the athletic challenge you set it. Well-balanced training stimuli lead to increased performance capability: the demands on your body should be neither too high nor too low. Ideal training stimuli are precisely tailored to an athlete's personal fitness level. In competitive sports, sports scientists create training plans incorporating a chain of perfectly coordinated stimuli designed to help top athletes achieve maximum performance within a certain period of time.

A brief introduction for beginners and resumers

Are you new to sports, or just getting going again after a long period of inactivity? Even if you have done sports before, you can't force quick progress when you start up again – especially not by taking on an overambitious workload. In sport, quality comes from quantity, because if you try to set stimuli in too rapid a sequence, your capabilities will only decline. Your body needs time to recuperate and will protest any attempt to overtax it by tiring quickly. If the interval between training sessions is too long, on the other hand, your fitness level will also decrease. But a lack of motivation is rare with beginners; instead, sports novices often have a tendency to overdo training at the start.

Smart athletes take regular breaks and challenge their bodies with just the right doses of training.

Training with care: Relaxation counts!

Take time to rest, because relaxation is part of your formula for success. While you are resting after training, your body is readying itself for new adventures.

If you want to train systematically and increase your performance slowly but surely, this can only be achieved with a sensible alternation of training sessions and relaxation phases. Be patient and don't forget that it will take a while for you to build up a solid foundation. Consistent endurance training leads to an optimisation of the musculature only after two years.

After this time has elapsed, your fine blood vessels (capillaries) will also have developed more branches and will be able to supply the body with oxygen more rapidly. In the muscles, you will have an increased amount of enzymes ready to go to work for you, your carbohydrate storage capacity will have risen, and the breakdown of stored fat will be functioning better. Even the mitochondria, the small "power plants" in our cells, will have multiplied and will contribute to a smooth and efficient aerobic energy metabolism.

You train regularly – and how does your body react? It puts everything you need at your disposal during training and girds itself in its "free time" for new athletic feats. Your body is very busy even on resting days: while you're lying on the sofa, your body is refilling its energy stores and repairing the fine structures of the muscles. It is thus reacting with increased activity to the training stimulus that you have given it.

Listen to your heart!

How can you be sure to challenge your body to just the right degree? Just listen to your heart, because when it begins to race, your body is being overstrained by the exercise you are doing. If you walk too fast, the cardiovascular system can no longer supply your muscles with sufficient oxygen. So your pulse is what tells you whether you have found the right tempo or are moving too fast.

Is your heart pounding? Your training will only bear fruit if you choose the tempo that is right for you.

An inadequate supply of oxygen will soon put the brakes on your activity of its own accord. Your muscles will feel fatigued, because without oxygen, they cannot efficiently turn glucose into energy. The waste product that results from this process, lactic acid, finally disables the muscles almost completely and forces you to stop training. When muscles are forced to work without oxygen, you have reached what is called the anaerobic zone. In endurance training, however, your goal is to work within the aerobic zone, in which adequate oxygen is available to your musculature. In this zone, the "operating materials" of fat and sugar can be burned more completely, avoiding the formation of lactic acid in amounts that detract from your performance. The so-called threshold pulse is the value at which muscles start to suffer from oxygen deprivation and switch from burning fat to burning sugar. Sugar is a quicker way to get energy, but the amount available in the body at any one time is limited. In medical lactate tests, the body's stress limits are determined by testing the blood. The results can provide important clues on how to design a future training plan.

Sore muscles or walking to your heart's content? A lactate test will show you where your limits are.

Training in the aerobic zone

- ❏ *Involves movement in conditions of excess oxygen.*
- ❏ *Fat and sugar supply energy.*
- ❏ *Only a small amount of lactic acid is produced.*
- ❏ *The acid/base balance is intact, muscles do not become fatigued.*
- ❏ *You achieve optimal training effects and improve your health.*

Training in the anaerobic zone
(for competitive athletes only)

- ❏ *Involves movement in conditions of oxygen depletion.*
- ❏ *Sugar supplies quick energy.*
- ❏ *High level of lactic acid develops in the blood.*
- ❏ *The muscles become "acidic" = fatigued.*
- ❏ *You overtax and overstrain the body. The immune system suffers.*

Excess pounds can't simply be shaken off in no time. Your maximum pulse will show you the right tempo for you.

Would you like to know the right training intensity for losing weight? You will likely be pleased to hear the following news: namely, that you will lose excess poundage best at a moderate tempo and not by pushing yourself to go at top speed. At low pulse rates – in the aerobic zone – our bodies burn the highest proportion of fat. After all, your muscles then require only a minimum amount of oxygen. The equation is easy to understand: when you walk faster, your body must supply your muscles with energy more rapidly, meaning it will choose sugar as its energy source. The fat stores will mostly go untouched. At 80 per cent of your maximum pulse rate, however, the muscles of a well-trained athlete use an impressive 90 per cent of fat. Therefore, the better the condition of an endurance athlete, the higher the proportion of fat that is burned during exercise.

Which pulse rate guarantees effective, health-promoting training, causing excess pounds to melt away? One way to approximate a sensible training heart rate is to start by determining your maximum pulse. If you are exercising at less than 55 per cent of your maximum pulse rate, then you are only moving at a moderate walk. While this promotes well-being and is doubtless good for your health, it only places moderate demands on your cardiovascular system and does not do much to challenge your muscles. If you exceed the upper limit of 85 per cent, you will hardly be able to achieve any positive health

Formula for approximate determination of maximum pulse rate

- ❏ *226 minus age = maximum heart rate (women)*
- ❏ *220 minus age = maximum heart rate (men)*

Training for health

Promotes circulation and relaxation, accelerates recovery processes.
Formula for determining training pulse rate:
- ❏ *Pulse rate (women): (226 minus age) x 0.55 minus 0.65*
- ❏ *Pulse rate (men): (220 minus age) x 0.55 minus 0.65*

Stabilisation zone

Trains basic endurance, increases fat burning during training sessions of between 45 and 60 minutes, promotes capillarisation by means of adaptation.
Formula for determining training pulse rate:
- ❏ *Pulse rate (women): (226 minus age) x 0.65 minus 0.75*
- ❏ *Pulse rate (men): (220 minus age) x 0.65 minus 0.75*

Progress zone

Effective cardiovascular training and maximum calorie burning. Carbohydrate stores in muscles increase, promotes lactate breakdown during exercise.
Formula for determining training pulse rate:
- ❏ *Pulse rate (women): (226 minus age) x 0.75 minus 0.85*
- ❏ *Pulse rate (men): (220 minus age) x 0.75 minus 0.85*

effects or the desired training results, because your muscles will soon become over-acidic and fatigued. So the trick is to aim for the "golden mean" – the range between the two extremes. You can calculate your approximate maximum pulse using a formula.

This figure will give you valuable information on how to plan your training. You can obtain more precise values by undergoing a lactate test, which can be performed in a clinic or institute for sports medicine.

Train wisely and systematically, and plan in time for your musculoskeletal system to get used to the new challenges.

Now you know the various exercise zones and their effects. With this information, you can avoid both under-challenging and overtaxing your body. Suitable "training bits" are the best guarantee for rapid progress and long-lasting exercise enjoyment. Take a clever approach to training and remember that tendons, ligaments, bones and cartilage need some time to grow strong enough for increasing sport activities in uneven terrain.

Optimal training for beginners: Training tips

How much time do you have to devote to Nordic Walking? In the first four weeks, walk only in the stabilisation pulse zone. Train two to three times a week for around 30 minutes and observe how your body responds. You will most likely notice when it has accustomed itself to the new activity. If you feel fit enough, you can then increase your training time to 45 minutes or one hour. If you wish, and if you have enough time in your schedule, increase your training sessions to four days a week. But that is not a must: it's better to walk regularly three times a week than to take on too much stress by trying to carve an extra training day out of a busy week. Training should above all be fun and should give you long-term pleasure. This can only happen if it doesn't become another source of stress in your life. Walking should be something you do for your own pleasure and well-being – no one is forcing you to do it!

Are you keeping a training diary yet? Taking regular notes on your training and how you are feeling can provide important clues later on, helping you to discover the causes behind any injuries or illnesses.

When are the best times to train? Make sure your training sessions are distributed as evenly as possible throughout the week, because it is important that there be enough time in-between for rest and regeneration. If you are very busy with your job, family and other responsibilities, the weekend is of course an ideal training time. Make a steady date with your walking poles every Saturday and Sunday. Then add in one day of your choice during the week, but not Friday or Monday. An appropriate weekly training cycle would be, for example, Wednesday, Saturday and Sunday. Tuesday, Friday and Sunday would be equally good.

Of course, you will want to see some genuine progress. Do you feel thoroughly fit after a few weeks of regular Nordic Walking? Then increase the intensity of your exercise a bit. If you pick up the tempo and can still converse without difficulty with your Nordic Walking companions – or yourself – then the speed is not too high for you. This little test is very useful, because without enough oxygen, the conversation would soon be over!

Heart rate monitors are not only tools for top athletes, but are also ideal for regulating the tempo of leisure-time training.

In order to optimise your training in the long term, however, regular pulse monitoring is also advisable. In addition to the relatively imprecise method of counting the pulse at your wrist or neck by hand, there are much more accurate methods available today. With a heart rate monitor, you will always know for certain whether you are exercising in the safe zone. You wear such a monitor like a watch, with the signal sent wirelessly via a transmitter in a band that you strap around your chest. You can then read your individual heart rate on the display. You start by saving the optimal heart rate zones you have determined using the test method of your choice (e.g. step test with determination of lactate levels and heart rate).

Pulse monitors can be purchased inexpensively today and are by all means a good investment, because your pulse not only provides regular information on your state of health, but also clues you in to the intensity of your training and your ability to regenerate. Some models can even store an entire training programme, including the heart rates measured. There are sophisticated computer programmes available these days for evaluating your training results.

TRAINING SENSIBLY

In order to program your heart rate monitor, you need to know your individual maximum heart rate. There are two ways to determine this. If you have not yet had an opportunity to have a lactate test carried out, you can determine an approximate value yourself using the self-test explained in the box below. For the most effective training, however, it is a great advantage to know the exact values.

Test methods for determining your individual maximum heart rate

❏ Determining your maximum heart rate using a self-test
Before conducting this self-test, please see your doctor for a thorough physical examination, in order to avoid any risks! If you can run, you can carry out this test at a running pace.
Procedure: Search out a route that is quite demanding, e.g. over hilly terrain. Walk or run 10 minutes to warm up, then walk or run for 10 minutes as fast as you are able. Begin slowly and increase your pulse rate every 60 seconds by 5 to 10 beats. Walk or run until you are exhausted. Take a look at your pulse monitor now and then during exercise. The highest value you reach is your personal maximum heart rate.

❏ A step test with lactate and heart rate measurement (lactate exercise test) at a sports science institute supplies much more precise values!

Ready for more? Training variations for advanced walkers

Can you now walk with confidence through any kind of terrain? Have you built up a good fitness level and developed an appetite for more? Then you can look forward to enjoying a wide variety of attractive exercise forms and training variations for energetic Nordic Walkers. Let's go – onward to new challenges!

What could be more natural than to first take it up a notch? Use your arms even more intensively and push off with a little more power from the balls of your feet. You will move forward faster and faster, soon reaching the threshold to a running stride. Simply start to jog, continuing to use the poles as you always do. The increased tempo not only requires that you be quite fit, but also demands a great deal of co-ordination. Especially tricky here is the smooth interplay of poles and limbs in rough terrain. You have to react quickly when an obstacle looms or the ground changes suddenly. Nordic Jogging provides an excellent change of pace, is lots of fun and increases the challenge to your muscles.

Demanding terrain, a change in tempo and trying out different techniques provide new stimuli.

51

An interesting variation to jogging with poles is fartlek (Swedish for "speed play"), a kind of unstructured interval training. There are no hard and fast rules here: simply change your tempo when you feel like it. Stroll through a field at a relaxed walking pace, and then run at turbo speed up a hill. Find a landscape that offers a variety of terrain and let yourself be inspired. Decide spontaneously to take a detour, the beautiful little path through the forest or a difficult rocky stretch. After a challenging phase, take it easy for a while and recoup your energy for the next fast

Staying loose but still walking with the necessary degree of alertness – when training in "adventurous" terrain, perfect co-ordination is the key.

sequence. The constant switching back and forth between fast and slow not only trains your coordination, but also makes your technique more dynamic and effective. In addition, the cardiovascular system and muscles are strengthened by this form of intensive training.

You can also try the double-pole technique now and again. You do this by sticking both poles into the ground parallel to one another. With a powerful push-off from your arms, you can now hop forward like a kangaroo.

Would you like to improve your speed, springiness and explosive force? Then get those poles swinging! First, walk until you are warmed up and then look for an even terrain free of holes and roots in which the poles can gain a firm purchase. Now you can take off ...

... in a jump-run:

Explosive legwork and an especially forceful push-off with the poles lets you take to the air in running jumps. Try to make your leaps high and long, and put all your power into it. After a short break, do another series. If you're still not out of breath, you can also take a small incline with a few running leaps.

When you perform more demanding movement sequences, your poles are subjected to special pressures.

... hopping on one foot:

Hop alternately on your right and left foot, raising the opposite knee as high as you can. Push off firmly with the poles, and swing your leg up as dynamically as possible.

... skating leaps:

Take off like a cross-country skier! Your leaping strides should be directed diagonally to each side and not straight forward. Use the poles – which should be angled diagonally to the sides – to assist your leg muscles in their work.

STRETCHING EXERCISES – THE RELAXATION PROGRAMME FOR YOUR MUSCLES

You have surely been advised at some point to incorporate some stretching exercises into your training routine. This is not a bad idea, because stretching actually does improve muscles' elasticity. The reason for this has not yet been satisfactorily explained, because the overall length of a muscle cannot be altered through stretching. By doing stretching exercises, endurance athletes endeavour to:

❏ Reduce risk of injury
❏ Improve recovery or regeneration of the muscles
❏ Balance out a potential disequilibrium between a muscle and its opposite, and as a consequence improve the sequence of movements in the sport in question

There is hardly a topic as much discussed as the proper stretching technique. But there are actually some well-grounded scientific findings that reveal the effects of the various methods.

Just to get it straight from the start: there is no one method with which all of these goals can be attained! Nevertheless, athletes still insist on stretching their muscles with an "all-round programme" and often end up doing more harm than good. The most common mistake is to do passive-static stretches right *after* training. A muscle is brought into a stretching position and held there for a few seconds. This is counter-productive, because the resulting compression of the capillaries hinders the circulation of blood in the muscle, blocking the removal of metabolic products.

Contrary to popular opinion, stretching after training unfortunately cannot prevent muscle pain, but can only aim at a rapid regeneration of the muscle tissue. The best way to do this is through active-dynamic stretching. In active-dynamic stretching

Could this be the shape of things to come?

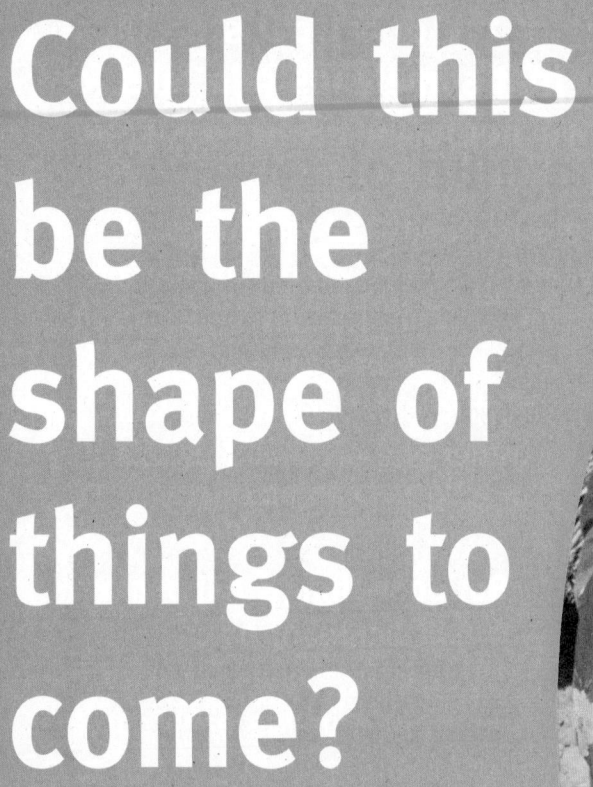
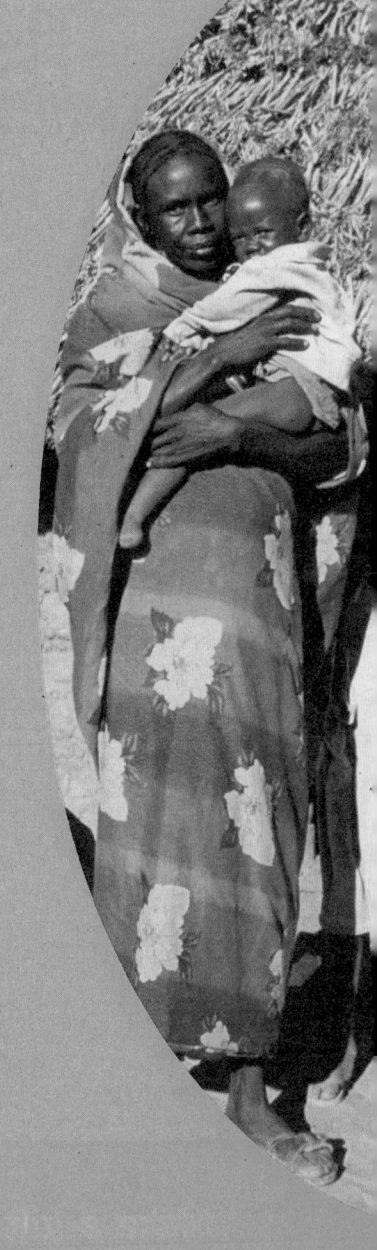

Look to the future, with Practical Action

People used to think that by the 21st century, hunger, famine and drought would be things of the past.

The sorry fact is that in our modern world a third of the population still have no reliable supply of food. An estimated 840 million people, including 234 million children, are malnourished.*

People need real answers to hunger – answers that will work not just for a day or a month, but for a lifetime.

That is why Practical Action does things differently. We help people use simple technologies – like crescent terraces – to change their lives. Our solutions involve local people at every stage. And we make sure that our practical answers will last, long into the future. For someone like Nafisa, that means her family will have enough to eat, every day.

Our answers work – but each one relies on the support of someone like you. Will you help us shape a better future?

Give £25 and you can help Practical Action use simple technology to overcome poverty today, tomorrow and for years to come. Thank you.

* Source: World Health Organisation Global Database on Child Growth

Whilst the stories in this leaflet are true, names and photos have been changed to protect the identity of individuals

Practical Action, The Schumacher Centre for Technology & Development, Bourton on Dunsmore, Rugby, Warwickshire CV23 9QZ UK
T: +44 (0)1926 634400 I F: +44 (0)1926 634401 I E: practicalaction@practicalaction.org.uk
W: www.practicalaction.org
Practical Action is the working name of Intermediate Technology Development Group Ltd.
Registered Charity No. 247257 Patron HRH The Prince of Wales, KG, KT, GCB

PRACTICAL ACTION
Technology challenging poverty

("intermittent stretching"), the movements are slow, rhythmic and controlled, focusing on the muscle to be stretched. This causes a contraction of the opposing muscle. If the calf is to be

Shortened muscles can lead to injuries. A gentle stretching programme helps prevent these from occurring.

stretched, for example, the shin muscle is simultaneously subjected to a light pull. A gradual increase in tension yields a so-called "gradual stimulus". Breathe out when moving in the stretching direction, and in when moving against the stretch. Perform two to three series of 15 to 20 controlled, gentle

forward and backward movements for each exercise. It is not necessary to stretch before you begin Nordic Walking; but do begin the first 10 to 15 minutes of your training at a fairly relaxed tempo. You will notice when you have reached your optimal "operating temperature" and can increase your speed and intensity.

Stretching after training

Aim: Regeneration, acceleration of metabolism, decreased muscular tension
Method: The active-dynamic stretching technique, which can be applied in all common stretching exercises (see for example the stretching exercises on pages 60 to 63). As an alternative or additional measure, "cooling off" slowly after training (i.e., relaxed Nordic Walking at a greatly reduced tempo) or actively loosening muscles in a swimming pool is recommended. Nothing promotes metabolism better than lying back and relaxing in pleasantly warm water. Also good for muscle relaxation are warm baths, massages and the sauna. Just be sure to combine a regeneration method of your choice with your Nordic Walking training!

How to strengthen weak muscles

A muscular dysbalance is said to exist when a muscle and its opposite have widely varying degrees of flexibility and strength. The best way to restore equilibrium is to train the weaker partner. The tension of the opposing muscle can be lowered by means of targeted physiological treatment.

Consult a physiotherapist for a selection of appropriate exercises to quickly remedy the dysbalance. Dysbalances that are left untreated for a long period of time can ultimately dampen your enjoyment of movement and lead to unpleasant tension or even chronic pain. Incidentally: dysbalances are commonplace in today's world. Due to the proliferation of desk jobs, in which the same one-sided posture is maintained day after day, many people have shortened chest and groin muscles and hamstrings.

The upper back muscles also fall into disuse with frequent sitting and slowly lose their strength. Strength-training exercises carried out in consultation with a competent physiotherapist or sports trainer, in combination with regular movement, are a good solution for this painful problem.

Stretching to improve flexibility

People often speak of an improvement in mobility as the result of stretching exercises. This is incorrect, because the term "mobility" refers to the range of movement of our bony joints, which can hardly be increased. Flexibility, by contrast, is the ability of the muscles, tendons, ligaments and joint capsules to tolerate changes in length. These elastic structures can be modified with the right exercise programme.

Passive-static stretching

In passive-static stretching, the muscle is gradually brought into the stretching position and held there. There should be no pain, only a slight pulling sensation. The stretched position should not be held any longer than 15 seconds. Scientific studies have shown that a longer stretching period does not lead to a greater improvement in flexibility.

Since the duration of the stretching stimulus is longer in passive-static exercises than in dynamic ones, the passive-static method of stretching is advisable if your goal is to increase flexibility in the shorter term. However, as has been noted above already, static stretches should under no circumstances be done directly following a training session, in order not to hinder muscular regeneration.

Perform the exercises of your choice as an independent training session after a short warm-up, through easy walking for example. Following your stretching routine, you should mobilise your joints again with some loose "walking out".

People naturally have varying degrees of flexibility. When it comes to stretching, women have a slight advantage over men.

A small selection of stretching exercises with and without poles

Neck and shoulder stretch

Chest stretch

Stand with your feet shoulder width apart. Bend your knees slightly in order to avoid arching your back. Hold the poles in your bent arms behind your head. Move the arms slowly a little bit further back. To stretch the chest muscles, pull your shoulder blades back and toward each other until you feel some tension in the chest area. Move your arms slowly back to the starting position and repeat the stretch.

Groin stretch

Beginning in a standing position, lunge forward with one foot, with your legs apart as far as possible. The rear leg makes contact with the ground only with the ball of the foot. Use your poles to support yourself at either side. Tighten your stomach muscles and tilt your pelvis forward and down, until you feel a slight pull in the groin area, then return to the starting position. Now repeat the same stretch with the other leg forward.

Side stretch

Grasp one or both poles. Stand with your feet shoulder width apart so that you have stable footing. Place one hand at either end of the pole/s and raise your arms above your head. Breathe in and bend gently to the right. Feel your left side stretching and then return to starting position, breathing in deliberately as you move upward again. Then stretch your right side by bending to the left.

Torso stretch

Holding the poles by the handles, bend far forward at the hips, setting the poles in front to support yourself. Move your feet back far enough that your arms and back are parallel to the floor. Elongate your spine, keeping your back straight and pushing your breastbone down toward the floor, then return to the starting position. Breathe in and out calmly.

Front thigh stretch

Support yourself on one pole and with the opposite hand pull one foot up behind you toward your buttocks. Tilt your pelvis slightly forward, avoiding arching your back by tightening your stomach and buttock muscles. You should feel a slight pull in the front muscle of the thigh. Move back to the starting position. Now switch sides and stretch the muscles in the other leg in the same manner.

Surface calf muscle stretch

Lean on both poles and go into a lunging position. The rear leg is straight and the heel is in contact with the ground. Move your hips and upper body carefully forward until you feel a good stretch. Do the same stretch with the other leg forward.

SUCCESSFUL WEIGHT LOSS WITH NORDIC WALKING

Regular endurance training does not lead to the dreaded "yo-yo effect", but rather helps you to remain stable at your ideal weight.

As you already know, Nordic Walking is a good choice of sport because it is one of the few that is kind to the joints. That is especially important for beginners, older people and those who are overweight. Without a problem and with gentle support, longer periods of training can be accomplished and calories expended from the very beginning.

Nordic Walking has a dual effect: it burns fat and it builds muscle. More muscle really pays off when it comes to keeping slim, because as you gain muscle the overall performance of your body and you use more energy. But only regular walking at a medium pace invites the body to use fat as an energy source. If trained at too high a speed or too intensively, the body will tap the carbohydrates stored in the muscles for quick energy instead of accessing fat stores.

How to lose pounds quickly and keep them off

With sufficiently long training sessions at a moderate tempo, you can stimulate your fat metabolism to kick into high gear. If you have already been walking for a while, you will profit from the so-called "after-burning" effect. Even once you have taken off your running shoes and gone on to other activities, your body will still be busy burning fat. This doesn't mean, however, that you can eat whatever you please. The important thing for losing weight is to burn more calories than you consume. Remember that on a normal day at the office that doesn't include an exercise session, you need only 2500 calories to get by, or even fewer. To find your basal metabolism rate (i.e. the energy consumed under strictly sedentary conditions), calculate one calorie per hour times body weight in kilograms (e.g. 24 hours times 65 kg = 1344 kcal).

As a gentle form of endurance exercise, Nordic Walking leads to increased fat burning, making it ideal for those looking to lose a few pounds.

Nordic Walking burns an average of 400 to 600 kcal per hour. You can therefore "earn" better calorie burning while having fun. Three to four endurance sessions per week, during which you walk for 45 to 60 minutes at a moderate tempo, are sufficient both for effective fitness training and for slimming. Support this favourable calorie balance with a sensible diet, and don't forget to drink enough.

Eat regularly and well!

There's no need to starve yourself in order to slim down! Go for quality nutrition and a balanced diet instead.

Look forward to meals! If you would like to lose weight successfully, forget about fasting and starvation diets. What counts is not the amount of carbohydrates and fat you consume, but rather their origins and quality. The best vitamins and nutrients are found in fresh fruit, vegetables and whole-grain products.

Nature's "original" foods are better than any pills or powders made industrially, because they have a balanced composition, are well tolerated by the body and guarantee good health. Vitamins "ignite" the metabolism, minerals help to renew cells and build bone. A variety of additional active substances promote well-being and strengthen the immune system. Whole foods help to ward off hunger pangs better because the fibre they contain makes you feel satisfied longer. A varied diet of whole foods, including high-quality vegetable oils, forms the basis for lasting fitness and gives you the energy you need for exercise activities. A good choice is vegetarian cuisine with its wide variety of delicious foods – after all, it's no coincidence that the term comes from the Latin word "vegetus", meaning "strong".

A word on so-called "light" products: there simply are no foods that guarantee slimness or weight loss. Light drinks offered by major food manufacturers should be enjoyed in moderation only. While they do not contain sugar, they do contain artificial sweet-

eners that can have unpleasant side effects. If the liver is "fed" with artificial sweetener, it reduces its release of sugar and instead holds onto the sugar from the blood. This lowers the blood sugar level and leads to hypoglycaemia, i.e. you feel weak and, at worst, shaky, with a strong urge to eat. Tests have shown that energy needs actually rise after people consume artificially sweetened foods.

In addition, the "fashion sweetener" has a few properties that are less than ideal: at temperatures over 30 degrees, which is the case in your stomach, it breaks down into the amino acids aspartate and pheylalanine, and also toxic methanol, which can cause headache, dizziness and cramps, among other things.

Craving something sweet? Choose natural foods and enjoy a "sweet break" without guilt.

Sport is a pleasurable "plus"

Grab your poles and explore the great outdoors: Nordic Walking with friends is even more fun.

Sport and a healthy diet are a successful duo. But try not to look at regular exercise simply as a way to stabilise your weight or as a (bothersome) chore. Exercise gives you an opportunity to leave your everyday cares behind and enjoy the wonders of nature. Endurance training such as Nordic Walking is a fun pastime that brings you many positive benefits.

Even though you greatly enjoy walking with poles, you should stay flexible in your sports activities so that you never get bored or get too much of a good thing. Take advantage of warm summer weather to go swimming, take a bike ride or gather friends together for a spontaneous game of outdoor volleyball. Look for ways to bring additional movement into your life and find out how good a little "extra" will do you. Even if, as a beginner, you may have some difficulties getting started: once sport becomes a firmly established part of your life, you will find you won't want to do without it.

Calories burned by Nordic Walking

How many calories you burn when walking with poles depends on the length of the route, the length of time that you walk and your body weight. In order to determine your actual energy use, you have to take into account the metabolic unit (MET). One MET is the oxygen intake of an adult while sitting. While Nordic Walking at a moderate pace (around 6 km/h) approximately 5 METs are used. So you need only multiply the METs for the respective exercise level by your body weight to arrive at the calorie use per hour for this intensity:

METs used x kg body weight x one hour =
calorie consumption for one hour

When you're walking through a beautiful landscape, time just flies. Regular excursions will have excess pounds melting away.

At a glance

❑ Exercise regularly and eagerly.

❑ Eat a diet of whole foods. Avoid processed food products and eat only whole grains.

❑ Read the ingredients on food packages and always choose whole foods: they not only taste better, they also satisfy your hunger better.

❑ Buy fresh fruit and vegetables whenever possible and let them inspire you to put together healthy and delicious meals.

❑ Enjoy preparing meals and take time to savour them.

❑ Eat regular meals and never skip lunch.

❑ Eat fruit as a between-meal snack instead of sweets.

❑ Make sure your acids and bases are in balance.

❑ Get enough sleep every night and avoid stress factors.

❑ Limit your coffee consumption.

❑ Don't smoke.

FIT THROUGH HEALTHY EATING

Water – Your key to health and fitness

Develop a sense of your body's needs and drink water at regular intervals. Thirst is your body's way of sending you a warning signal.

What do you drink when you're feeling thirsty? The optimal choice is plain water, the simplest and healthiest fitness drink in the world! Hand on your heart: how many other drinks do you consume every day and how low is the proportion of water in your diet? Your body requires around 2.4 litres of water every day, of which 1.5 litres needs to be consumed in the form

Clear water is simply irreplaceable. Pay attention to your water consumption and pay special attention to how often you drink diuretic beverages such as coffee and black tea.

of drinks. This recommendation is only a rule of thumb for minimal needs. If you perspire while working or exercising, the water lost thereby has to be replaced with an extra portion of liquids – at best with clear, still water. The human body consists of 75 per cent water, and water is therefore urgently needed for all metabolic processes.

Water is not only a component of all the cells in the body; it is also the only means of transport and dissolution for all the nutrients and other useful substances that we take in with our food. Without water, our bodily functions would come to a standstill. Water makes possible the vital elimination of metabolic products from the body, and is responsible for the exchange of materials between all our cells. It also plays a key role in regulating body temperature.

Every human being can go for a time without food. But without drinking, things very quickly become critical, because a deficit of water automatically entails a lack of certain minerals (sodium, chloride, potassium, magnesium, etc.) and trace elements (including zinc, copper and selenium). When exercising, the body loses more water than usual through sweating, and the human organism reacts to this loss very sensitively.

A fluid deficit of just 1 per cent of our body weight can already lead to measurable psychological and mental changes, expressed by means of physical weakness and a depressed mood. With a deficit of more than 2 per cent, endurance performance is affected, and the heartbeat becomes faster. From 4 per cent onward, the strength and coordination of an athlete declines noticeably. At 5 per cent depletion, disorders such as fatigue, apathy and muscle cramps appear. When fluids drop below this level, the condition of dehydration becomes life-threatening. Incidentally, the subjective feeling of thirst is not a reliable indicator of personal water needs, because most people only feel thirst starting at a deficit of 0.5 litres. For all these reasons, be sure to drink plenty of water, because water is truly the elixir of life.

Remember to take enough water with you every time you go Nordic Walking. Particularly at high temperatures, your body needs to compensate for water loss during exercise.

Plenty of liquids for well-being

❑ Don't think of drinking water as an annoying duty. Our ancestors had to walk for kilometres to find a pure spring from which to drink, and they enjoyed every drop. Water is a precious treasure!

❑ In the morning, right after you get up, drink a tall glass of water. This can come straight from the tap, because in most cities the water is of good to excellent quality.

❑ Carbonated water is not easy to drink and thus limits your consumption of liquids. Carbonation makes you feel satisfied too quickly – before you have had the chance to drink enough water. Choose still bottled water or tap water instead.

❑ Enjoy the purity and uniqueness of clear water. taste and feel how pure water quenches your thirst and does you good.

❑ Pay attention to what you drink: since coffee and black tea are diuretics, always drink a tall glass of water alongside them.

❑ Keep track of how much you drink. This is easiest if you place a large bottle of mineral water near your desk every morning. Not drinking any water from breakfast to lunch has consequences: your mental and physical performance decline rapidly – and your body suffers from a lack of fluids.

❑ If you drive your car to work, you should always have a bottle of water next to you on the passenger seat. Not one hour of the day should go by when you don't reach for your water bottle.

❑ The commonly heard protest "I can't drink that much!" is no excuse! Knowing what you now know about the importance of water for your overall well-being, you can relearn how to drink enough, and before long you will never want to do without your allotted portion of water again.

A sufficient quantity of water not only promotes your physical performance. It also keeps you wide awake on the job, helping you to deal with stress and achieve top performance.

Finding the right acid-base balance

Most active exercisers make sure they get enough vitamins and minerals, but forget to fine-tune the individual components of their diet. Experiencing list-lessness and weariness, both during everyday activities and while training, are often symp-toms of a disruption in the equilibrium between acids and bases in the body. This places a burden on the metabolism and has a negative effect on the body's ability to regenerate. Keep in mind that an optimally functioning metabolism is the foundation for your athletic achievements.

Acids are either formed in the body through metabolism, or they are consumed when we eat acidic or acid-forming foods. For the body's acid balance, the critical question is whether the acids are volatile and leave the body again quickly (such as fruit acids contained in vegetables or fruit) or whether they oxidise easily and can be converted into other substances, for example sulphuric acid.

Snacks with an alkaline pH give you energy.

76

If the body cannot rid itself of excess acid by way of the lungs, kidneys, skin or intestines, it stores them in the connective tissue, in cartilage and tendons, which are then substantially weakened and much more susceptible to injury.

In order to contain the excess development of acids in the body, you should concentrate on foods with a basic pH (see the following table) and take into consideration the schedule by which the digestive organs complete their work. If you ignore the "peak times" of the stomach and intestines, you will put the brakes on your metabolism. As a general rule: the later the hour, the slower the metabolism works. Therefore, supply your stomach with fibre (raw fruits and vegetables) during its most active hours – i.e., morning and early afternoon – and go without salads and fruit in the evening. A salad plate eaten in the evening is anything but a light meal for your digestive system. The fibre can no longer be broken down optimally in the small intestine, which is not operating up to speed, and it will ferment into alcohol.

Eat in rhythm with your digestive system. Fatigue and drops in performance are often the result of an unfavourable diet plan.

This is why it's a good idea to eat raw foods during the first half of the day if possible, and to eat your salad with lunch instead of your evening meal. A perfect lunch, rich in bases and nutrients, will contain the largest possible proportion of fresh, steamed vegetables, along

with carbohydrates in the form of whole grains, grain products (noodles) or potatoes. If you add the soy product tofu, for example, your meal now offers high-quality protein, magnesium, potassium and a large portion of calcium, which is up to 40 per cent reabsorbable. In comparative studies with animal protein, soy reduced calcium loss by 40 per cent.

An ideal supper – which should not be eaten any later than three to four hours before bedtime – contains for example base-rich steamed vegetables with noodles, or vegetable soup.

How to break down acids while bathing

The foods we eat are not the only source of the acids in our bodies. Intensive exercise also causes a greater or lesser quantity of lactic acid (lactate) to form in the muscles and tissues, which must be "neutralised" through the intake of bases by way of food or drink (e.g. "Basica" mineral supplement). A bath to regulate the acid-base balance (made e.g. by adding 3 tablespoons of bi-carbonate of soda to the bathwater) is an appealingly simple and extremely effective way to help the body excrete lactate through the skin.

If you take this kind of bath directly after training, you won't have to worry about suffering from "heavy legs" or fatigue. It will also keep your body from "plundering" the mineral deposits stored in your bones, cartilage and tendons, which are tapped in cases of "emergency".

Remember to give yourself some time to rest after any physical activity, because stress and anger also cause the body to produce acids. Don't forget to drink plenty of clear water after every

training session, and avoid consuming only soft drinks or other alternatives to water. Your body itself is 75 per cent water – if you neglect to replenish this fluid conscientiously, your body will conserve water in the digestive and detoxification processes, in deacidification, and even in the central nervous system and the spinal discs.

Soaking in a bath is not only relaxing, it also optimises the acid-base balance in your body.

A selection of acidic and base-rich foods

Base-rich foods

milk, buttermilk, whey, soy and soy products, fruit, vegetables (with the exception of Brussels sprouts and artichokes), white beans, potatoes, mushrooms, herbal teas

Neutral foods

butter, cream, noodles, rusk, almonds, hazelnuts

Acid-rich foods

hard cheese, margarine, quark, cereal, rice, peanuts, brazil nuts, walnuts, fish and seafood, meat and sausages, canned vegetables and preserved fruit, sweets, coffee and black tea, alcoholic drinks

Fast food, processed foods and drinking too much coffee all have a negative effect on the body's acid-base balance. Eat calmly, make sure to eat enough alkaline foods and allow yourself time simply to relax.

Keep moving and protect your body with vital nutrients

One of the benefits when we participate in sports is that we bolster our immune system. Moderate endurance exercise does more than increase muscular circulation; it also delivers an increased supply of oxygen throughout the entire body. This helps the cells of the immune system do their work. Nutrition that

A strong immune system arms you against diseases and strengthens your ability to tackle job challenges.

81

fortifies the immune system brings with it additional benefits that protect our health and vigor. Healthy eating begins with whole foods that are not over-processed, and fresh foods that are either not heated, or at the very least not overcooked. These strengthen the body. The essential nutrients contained in whole foods can do even more. They stabilize the vital immune system and protect it against intruders. In addition to minerals and trace elements, vitamins are particularly important for the immune cells. Vitamins are organic compounds, which, because the organism cannot produce them on its own, need to be added to the diet in small amounts. Metabolic problems can occur if the body is vitamin deficient. A complete lack of certain vitamins can, depending on the level of the body's own supply, even lead to death. In contrast, too much of any vitamin is only seldom dangerous. Vitamins are therefore an invaluable component of our food.

Snacking without guilt: fresh fruit is full of healthy nutrients and fosters greater vitality.

Vitamins work within the body controlling the metabolism and serving as its catalyst. They perform specialized functions within the organism. They influence the transformation of nutrients into energy, the immune system, hormone regulation, the body's natural detoxification and the enzymes that play a role in every biological process. This is why human beings need vitamins.

Vitamins are divided into two categories according to their characteristics. A, D, E and K are the fat soluble vitamins, while B1, B2, B5 and B6, C, H, Folic Acid and Niacin are water soluble. Their biological functions are correlated with their solubility. Fat soluble vitamins are stored in relatively large quantities in the liver and fatty tissues of the body. This storage system can provide the necessary vitamins even if the organism is undernourished for an extended period of time. This ability to store large quantities can, in extreme cases of overdose, lead to hypervitaminosis – i.e., poisoning. With the exception of B12, water soluble vitamins are not stored in the body. Any excess beyond the current needs of the body is simply excreted in the urine. Because some vitamins are quite sensitive to certain environmental conditions (light, heat, etc.), the vitamin content of food frequently varies widely based on the manner of food preparation.

Normally, a balanced diet guarantees the necessary supply of vitamins, as long as the daily menu includes lots of fresh products. Fresh foods also offer the advantage of containing sufficient quantities of minerals. Additional vitamin supplements are usually not necessary. Given a healthy diet, vitamin deficiencies occur for the most part only when a specific disease is present. Ideally, you should take in small doses of vitamins throughout the day in the form of vegetables, fruit or salad.

Eat plenty of fresh foods – let yourself be tempted by the wide range of seasonal fruits and vegetables on offer.

You can start taking the initiative already in winter. Plant seeds for legumes and grains and set them on a windowsill or a sunny spot on a shelf. These will quickly produce vitamin-rich sprouts.

These are an ideal ingredient for salads and are delicious on a slice of bread or as a steamed vegetable. You can raise mung beans, alfalfa and chick peas in a specialized sprout container (available in shops) or in preserve jars and harvest them daily.

The amount of vitamins and minerals found in dried grain, seeds or beans is multiplied many times in their sprouts, and others are present only in the sprouts (for example, vitamin C and Magnesium). The minerals and trace elements are also better absorbed by the human digestive tract from sprouts than from vegetables and grains. This is good news for all of those for whom whole grain bread lays a bit heavy in the stomach.

Fresh, homemade juices are nutritious revitalisers. When it comes to mixing ingredients, let your fantasy run wild!

Vitamin C – Power for the Body

"Take a lot of vitamin C!" We've practically internalised this advice. Together with the trace element Selenium and vitamin E, vitamin C protects cell membranes. This best known of all vitamins also supports the granulocytes that defend against bacteria. These immune cells have to be re-supplied with vitamin C continually in order to, for example, fight off intruding viruses. It's not citrus fruits that offer the most vitamin C, nor blackcurrants, but the sea buckthorn. In 1940 researchers discovered ascorbic acid in the berries of the – at that time – barely noticed shrub. Depending on the origin of an individual plant, 100 grams of the fresh fruit contain up to 1000 milligrams of

A delicious treat for any taste – it just takes a minute to prepare healthy snacks packed full of vitamins.

vitamin C, averaging 450 milligrams. Its other components, vitamin E, beta carotene and vitamins B1, B2, B6 and B12, stave off
infection and stimulate the circulatory system. Unsweetened,
buckthorn berries taste somewhat "strong"; they're best sweetened with a little honey. Buckthorn juice can be added to muesli,
soy milk, yogurt and quark. It also works well mixed with other
fruit juices as part of a cocktail.

Why can't our body produce its own vitamin C, given that it
seems to need it in considerable quantities? Evolution researchers found the answer to this question in our ancestors' teeth.
Wear patterns on molars show the intense chewing charac-
teristic of a plant-based diet. Clearly, nourishment from plants
played a dominant role in the nutrition of early humans, not only
in the hunter-gatherer period, but also later in the agricultural
age. Food scientists Leitzmann and Hahn explain the differences:
"Anyone who relies primarily on such a diet doesn't need to
produce vitamin C on their own. In addition to humans, apes and
guinea pigs have also lost the ability to produce vitamin C in the
course of their development. Meat eaters, in contrast, have
retained this ability. Meat doesn't contain vitamin C, which makes
its manufacture by the body absolutely necessary."

Food scienctists have no one point of view regarding the correct
dosage of this most prominent essential nutrient. In the UK, the
Committee on Medical Aspects of Food and Nutrition Policy
(COMA) recommends 40 milligrams; the World Health Organi-
zation (WHO) considers 30 milligrams daily sufficient. Generally,
regular consumption of fresh fruit easily supplies the require-
ments of a healthy person. It is not necessary to take vitamin C
supplements in addition to a whole food diet; in fact, excess
vitamin C is not stored, but is simply excreted in the urine. If
vitamin C is nevertheless to be consumed for health reasons, it
should be well spread out over the course of the day.

The vitamin C content of fruit and vegetables

Black currants	189mg/100g
Parsley	166 mg/100g
Green/red peppers	approximately 140 mg/100g
Broccoli	115 mg/100g
Fennel	93 mg/100g
Cauliflower	73 mg/100g
Kiwifruit	71 mg/100g
Watercress	59 mg/100g
Oranges	50 mg/100g
Lemons	30 mg/100g

A colourful cornucopia for gourmets: go on a culinary journey of discovery and treat yourself generously to the gifts of nature's garden!

Nutritional supplements – Yes or no?

You can find them these days in every supermarket, sitting on the shelves in colourful packaging. Antioxidants and vitamins are the darlings of the pharmaceutical industry. They sell themselves very well, indeed, thanks to health conscious customers. Reason enough, therefore, to take a close look at minerals and trace elements. Does it make sense to supplement your diet with powders and tablets? The call is for "prevention" and the buyers' favorite products are the minerals and trace elements. A look at

A simple formula for success: with a balanced diet of whole foods and plenty of exercise, it's easy to stay healthy and fit.

the letters to the editor column in the relevant sports magazines shows that even people who take these substances are uncertain as to the correct dosage. How much magnesium, for example, is recommended, and does it make sense to take these minerals in powder or tablet form as supplements to one's normal diet? For once, let's put those minerals and trace elements right under the microscope.

There's no need to fear deficiencies! Trace elements are effective even in the smallest quantities.

Minerals are indispensable for the mechanisms that stimulate our nerves and muscles, ensure a constant moisture level in our cells and blood vessels, and build strong bones and teeth. All minerals are water soluble, and they are classified as either trace elements or as macro-nutrients. The trace elements – iron, iodine, selenium, copper, chromium, molybdenum, silicon, fluoride, bromine, cobalt, manganese, zinc and vanadium – are found in the human body only in very small amounts. Only the smallest "traces" are needed. If we consume too much of these, particularly selenium, copper and cobalt, they are poisonous. Trace elements are most commonly found as charged particles (ions) in the form of a simple salt or as active parts of large molecules in the blood. In this way, cal-

cium and phosphorus, for example, together with iron, bond with oxygen within the bones.

Macronutrients (natrium, phosphorus, magnesium and calcium) are found in the organism in comparatively larger quantities. Because, as with vitamins, the body can't produce them on its own, we have to ingest them. The daily requirement for macro-minerals is a little over 100 milligrams.

Although a very few milligrams or micrograms are already more than an adequate supply, trace elements are nevertheless especially important for bodily functions. Many enzymes (protein molecules that instigate and support chemical reactions within the body) can only function, for example, in the presence of "their" highly specialised trace element.

The balance between trace elements and minerals (macronutrients) is very sensitive. From this point of view, nutritional supplements are often negative intruders in the body, in addition to being an unnecessary strain on the shopper's budget. If you choose to increase your intake of one substance, you should be aware that in doing so, you reduce the absorption of one of the others. A well-known example involves the inverse relationship between calcium and magnesium. When athletes take calcium supplements as a prophylactic measure because they want strong bones, they block the body's absorption of magne-

An overdose of synthetic vitamins intervenes in the delicate balance between the various nutrients and can have undesirable effects.

sium. Conversely, repeatedly consuming magnesium powder hinders the absorption of calcium. Although a little "extra" zinc is often recommended as protection from infection and for stabilization of the immune system, it can, if taken over a longer period of time in supplement form, bring about the opposite effect and, in addition, lessen the absorption of copper.

Nutritional supplements, yes or no? It is better to hold back, because substitution is a tightrope walk. Extra preparations only make sense for a clearly determined period of time, and only if there really is a serious deficiency. Balanced, whole food meals are usually more than enough to keep an active, athletic person energetic and fit.

Nature instead of substitutes: as a rule, a sufficient quantity of vitamins and minerals can be obtained by eating whole foods.

THE BEST MOTIVATION TIPS

*L*et's set the record straight at the outset: no one is motivated all the time. Even the most passionate sports enthusiast and professional athlete will occasionally have to fight against a lack of desire. Tying on the running shoes can take a lot of effort on those rainy, cool days or after a long day at work. But it's worth it to get out there nevertheless. Nordic walking improves your mood and makes you feel good!

How to outwit laziness and lack of desire

How about trying out a new walking route? No day is like any other. Keep your training programme versatile and exciting!

Do you walk, like many others, in the late afternoon or evening? If so, make every effort to begin exercising right after work. Perhaps you can bring your shoes and Nordic Walking poles to the

office with you and turn your route home into your training track. Be careful! Once you settle in and make yourself comfortable at home, you'll likely find it infinitely difficult to rouse yourself for a walk. So put your bag down and get right into your training shoes!

One day you may find that you have a particularly strong desire for a break in your training, or for a change of routine. When that urge strikes, replace your planned Nordic Walk with another (athletic) activity of your choice. How about a relaxing swim, or an easy bike ride to visit friends? Or simply put your legs up and relax. Sports should enrich your life, not become a compulsory enterprise. Pay attention to how you are feeling. In addition, during the winter months, cross-country skiing – the "original" Nordic Walking – is tremendous fun. And have you ever tried inline skating? This discipline can also be practiced with poles, a sport known as Nordic Blading. Variety is the best motivator!

A rigid training plan can dull your desire for exercise. Stay flexible and open to training alternatives.

Don't walk when you're hungry; that's no fun at all. Anyone who walks right after work should under no circumstances skip lunch, and should also eat a healthy snack between meals. Fruit bars, nuts and dried fruit (such as apricots or raisins) are easily kept in the office in your handbag or desk drawer. A banana also calms a hungry stomach. Don't forget to drink a tall glass of clear water one half hour before exercising.

If you plan your exercise appoint- ment in advance, you won't be able to back down so easily. Make a small note to yourself to strengthen your motivation.

An essential bit of business: have your Nordic Walking sessions planned already at the beginning of each week. When do you have time for exercise? Note these dates on your calendar. In our often busy professional and family lives, appointments are frequently rescheduled or cancelled. Perhaps you can use these unexpectedly free time slots for a tension-easing sport inter- mezzo. Try to always keep the basic Nordic Walking gear stored in your office or car, where it is readily available. You can easily stash your poles in the car. Do you tend to back out shortly before your exercise time? Then make it into a firm obligation. Does a good friend Nordic Walk already? Maybe he or she

would like to climb on board, too. That fixed walking appointment might well become one of the high points of your week, because Nordic Walking is a social sport.

Another way to stay interested in Nordic Walking over time is to become a "trailblazer". Covering the same training route all the time is boring for even the most dedicated walker in the long term. Cast your net further and discover new territory. A change of scenery gives you a new training program every time you walk. Try to alternate long training sessions with shorter, more intensive ones. Travel into the mountains and try out your jumps!

Do you have a hiking map of your area? Explore unknown territory and discover new favourite routes.

Picture credits

Photographs: Jump photo agency

Illustrations: Diana Billaudelle